To my fellow nurses. You inspire me every day.

Introduction

Welcome to Love Nursing! Living the Dream. I am excited to write this mini advice book especially, for new nurses. I hope to share it with nurses as they come to my unit and I'll probably print multiple copies to give out to the different hospitals I work at. The other reason I am writing this is that nursing has given me so much happiness and joy that when I see others starting their journey, I want them to love it as much as I do. Here is my attempt to do that.

A brief background about myself... My name is Yolande La Belle BSN RN and I have loved nursing for over 36 years. I have worked in Pediatrics, done some home health nursing, worked for a Doctor's office, and found my niche in Neonatal Intensive Care where I have been for the last 26 years and still love it, find meaning and fulfillment, and hope to share my tips and hacks on being the nurse you always wanted to be. These suggestions can make your journey worthwhile. Your life, when looked back on, will make you proud of your contribution. So let's jump in!

Welcome! Are you a new nurse? I salute you, Gladiator. You'll experience some of the highest highs (saving a life) and the lowest lows (losing a life). But you can navigate this journey as an adventure and not let the lows knock you off your path, though you may find some course changes as you find your niche, and that's good.

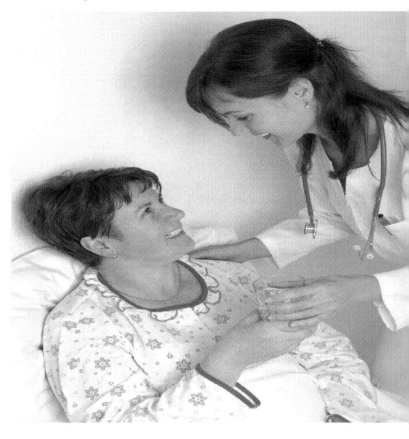

Cultivate Compassion

Compassion is at the very heart of nursing care. Nurses often feel the calling to help others. If you are here just for a paycheck, then you're probably in the wrong profession. Nursing with compassion gives meaning, satisfaction, and purpose to your career making a difference to those you touch. And you will find that you have the opportunity to touch many lives and those lives touch others in a ripple effect that reaches beyond what you can see. It's mind-boggling the difference you can make. Small acts of kindness can make a significant difference in someone's healing journey. Compassion leads to connection. Connection with your patients and your coworkers creates fulfillment in your career life.

The queen of work-life balance

Maintaining a Work-Life Balance

Nursing can be emotionally and physically draining so take care of YOU!

We all know the "shoulds". We "should" all over ourselves. "I should eat healthy, I should exercise, I should get enough sleep...". I too have been where I'm too tired to care and reach for junk food, veg on the couch and miss out on sleep, especially us night shifters. You can't give from an empty cup. Recognize that by taking care of yourself, you can better care for others and sustain your passion for the nursing profession. So what can I do that helps keep me going?

Set boundaries. I've watched nurses give so much to work and not enough to themselves that they burn out. Nurses are givers. It is common to put everyone and everything before yourself. Long hours and extra shifts can take their toll. It feels as if there aren't enough hours in a day to get everything done.

Be mindful. When you are at work, be at work. When you are at home, be at home. Keep your mind focused on the task at hand. Letting it drift to what you "need" to do will bring stress to your mind. Focus on what you are doing right now. You will take care of everything as it comes along, one step at a time.

Sometimes I even coach myself saying as I finish each step, "The next step is...". I find my mind calms and I progress smoothly.

Prioritize tasks based on urgency and importance. Don't hesitate to delegate when necessary. For example, when we admit a new patient, everyone available jumps in to help. Many hands make it go quickly while building the team up and reducing stress because the load is shared. Don't be that nurse who sits around not helping when you see others running around. Be the nurse to jump in and help. That keeps balance and camaraderie at work. I have stayed so long at this particular job because of the people, my NICU family.

A few of my NICU family

Spend time with people you care about. Take the time
to be with your family, friends, and even your fur

family. And when you are with them, really be with them. Let work fall away. Focus on your time with them. Time is your most valuable commodity. When that time is gone, it is gone. You don't want to look back and regret missing the time spent with those you love. For example, if you have children, enjoy all the day-to-day moments because you will be surprised at how quickly it will pass. I know you have heard this from older folk before, but a life living and appreciating the place you are in **right now** with your loved ones doesn't lead to regrets but rather wonderful memories. And if you have a fur family, they can be highly amusing and add much to your life. Stop and appreciate it. That unconditional love is very healing.

Our fur family can contribute so much to our lives too. This is my cat Jaimie.

Spend some of your precious time doing what makes you happy and do what recharges your battery. Find hobbies that help you create something or learn something. Get outdoors and enjoy a hike, a walk, or whatever sounds good to you. There are so many options and I suggest you explore many. If you can include someone with you, all the better! By all means, include spiritual activities that feed, nourish, and uplift your soul. Placing God front and center grounds me and gives me direction.

Recharge with friends and family!

Get outdoors!

What I find least helpful are the time suckers of social media and binge-watching TV. However, I enjoy those, so limiting the amount of time I allow for those is a must. I have found success with either limiting myself to a certain amount of time per day or giving myself a day off when I can binge to my heart's desire.

Celebrate victories and milestones, both small and large. Nursing is filled with countless moments of joy. Take the time to acknowledge these moments. Finding these moments can reignite your passion for nursing. It could be as simple as a smile from an infant, a successful outcome, or a meaningful connection. Celebrate your achievements. Moments like positive feedback from a patient, a coworker, or a supervisor. Don't just blow it off. Stop for a moment to feel gratitude. Say a sincere "thank you". Have you just learned a new skill? Maybe you placed your first IV or every time you place an IV, take a moment to appreciate your ability. Have you achieved a higher degree or milestone? Celebrate! Reward yourself with a happy dance, a nice meal, out on the town, a trip, whatever. Recognize that you have done well and give yourself that pat on the back. There will be times that try to bring you down so counteract those by noticing all the good things that too often go unnoticed.

Recognizing 35 years in nursing!

Balancing your work-life journey includes self-care, **learning** to nourish your body, mind, and spirit, cultivating resilience, and a deep sense of well-being that radiates from within and enriches every aspect of your life. Learn to be mindful and present in the moment. Reign that mind of yours back in as it tries to jump 5 steps ahead. Practice. Practice. Practice. You are worth the effort and so is your peace of mind.

Embrace Continuous Learning

Be curious. Curiosity can lead to places you have not foreseen. Imagination is the cornerstone of new ideas and learning stimulates curiosity and imagination.

Attend conferences, especially with your coworkers as this builds friendships. Good times are to be had as you travel together. Many conferences are located at tourist places so you have an opportunity after the classes for fun and getting to know each other outside of work which I highly recommend. Learning keeps your career engaging, and exciting and builds relationships as you learn and play together.

Learning helps you stay flexible and adaptable because nursing is a changing, growing field with discoveries, new technology, new medications, and standards of care that change as we learn better ways to care for our patients. For example, just since I have been in nursing, we have gone from paper charting to computer charting and the computer system of charting has changed to different systems over the years and is about to change again. That has been intimidating to me at times. Again, celebrate your victories with every new skill you learn.

Nursing is not a static and boring job. Embrace change. **It is happening for you, not to you.** You too will grow and change and that's a good thing. Always progressing, even baby steps, is rewarding.

Go beyond your comfort zone, for just on the other side, is everything you want. Don't let fear or insecurity stop you from trying new things. Be Bold! Be Brave! I know it can be scary. Overcoming "scary" creates self-confidence and our greatest growth. You can do it! First, you believe it, then you do it and that will reinforce your belief. And on you go.

Fred Rogers said, "When I was a boy and I would see scary things in the news, my mother would say to me, "Look for the helpers. You will always find people who are helping."

You are a helper. In a scary situation, find a way to help.

Stay Positive and Be Resilient

You can overcome almost anything by staying positive and being resilient. Reflect on positive moments. Even in challenging situations, there are silver linings or lessons to be learned.

Thrive in your career by focusing on the meaningful impact you make in the lives of others. I currently work in NICU (neonatal intensive care unit) and caring for these "littles" from birth to discharge home is so rewarding. And now, I can even follow them on Facebook when the parents add me as their friend. I have the privilege of watching them grow up and thrive and know that I had a hand in helping get them off to a good start.

Took care of these 2 when they were infants and later their mom reached out to reconnect. Touched my heart.

Not every story has a happy ending. Learn from those experiences in which you cannot change and continue on your path while you practice being positive and resilient. It will take practice. And that's okay. Be patient with yourself. Be gracious to yourself. Lean on your coworkers. They have been there too. Being there for each other will build you up.

Be there for each other.

Every challenge is an opportunity for growth. Not just the challenges at work but in life. Be open to learning from every experience. There is always something to learn but sometimes you must look for it. Ask yourself, "What can I learn from this?" Just asking that question to yourself refocuses your mind. It can take your mind off the anger, off the denial, the feelings of being overwhelmed, or fear or panic or whatever. "What can I learn from this?" **Really** think about it. And then, what is my next step right now? We come back to being present and mindful in that moment. It is okay to feel what you feel. But when it starts to feel overwhelming, like grief, for example, focus on the present moment. Not the past, not the future, just this moment, one moment at a time and you will get through. Remember, this too will pass because nothing stays the same and you will figure out what can be learned from it. Then move on. Do not dwell in the past. Learn and move on. I believe these challenges are happening for you, not to you. Just that little tweak in your belief can make a big difference in your attitude helping you stay positive and be resilient. Don't ask God to make life easier, ask him to make you better, stronger, and more resilient.

Foster Gratitude and Express Appreciation

Take the time to express gratitude toward your coworkers. A simple "thank you" or note of appreciation can go a long way in fostering a positive work environment and strengthening relationships.

Reflect on positive moments and experiences. **Consider keeping a gratitude journal**. Keep a folder of any cards or notes of appreciation. Reflection on these positive moments reinforces the value and impact of your work. As they accumulate over time, you see, feel, and touch the difference you are making. Need a lift, a boost, a feel-good pick me up? Then look back in your journal and reread those times that made you feel good. But you have to write them down to save them because as much as you think you will remember it all, you won't. Even a pocket-size notebook in your bag or locker can give you quick access to jot it down.

Find your Niche

Explore different areas of nursing to discover your passionate place. Perhaps it will be in neonatal, pediatrics, surgery, oncology, labor and delivery, geriatrics, community care, forensics, in a hospital, in a Doctor's office, or even on a cruise ship. You may even want to use your skills on a global scale participating in medical missions, disaster relief efforts, or serving the underserved. The possibilities are endless. Have fun exploring. Your niche may even change over the years. How cool is that? Being a nurse can lead down so many roads. There are so many possibilities so keep going and enjoy the journey. Find what you love.

Finding your niche allows you to focus your efforts and excel in an area that aligns with your interests and strengths. Making a difference every day in an area you enjoy is so rewarding. Love your work by working at what you love. This is not new. Confucius said, "Choose a job you love and you will never have to work a day in your life."

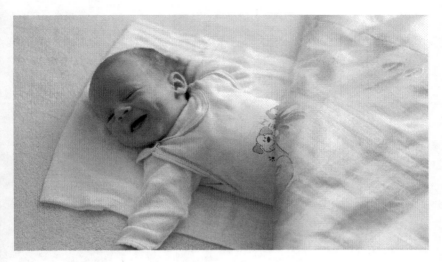

Build Friendships

Take the time to foster friendships in the workplace. I call mine, "My NICU Family". At work, you could make a list of birthdays and post it. Get together outside of work. For example, some ideas we have done included holiday get-togethers, going for a night out or breakfast after a night shift, karaoke potlucks at each other's homes, cooking class where one of us shares how to make a favorite recipe (we have learned some great ethnic foods). Some like to go on hikes together. We have gone on short trips together, and gone to conferences together. We have gotten together to make crafts, like Christmas candles. The ideas are endless. You may find some who become your lifelong friends and what a blessing will be.

More NICU family

Find your people. Seek friendships with other positive people. Surround yourself with them. Have you heard the saying, "You are the sum of the 5 people you hang around with?" Choose wisely grasshopper...

Our companions will influence us more than we realize. Ask yourself if they uplift and inspire you or bring you down? The energy of positive, kind, gracious individuals is contagious and those connections enrich our lives. Distance yourself from toxic influences as they are also contagious. To do this, you must evaluate your inner circle. You may need to make some changes. For your mental and emotional health, I hope that you do.

We have all seen both positive and negative nurses and I hope you gravitate to and emulate the positive ones. It's all too easy to fall into bad habits and takes a bit of effort to catch yourself and change your path. Don't go to the dark side. If you start drifting, catch it, and laugh to yourself, saying, "I will not go to the dark side." Being able to laugh at our little follies lightens the load. Humor is a fantastic coping mechanism. Epictetus said, and you have probably heard it, "He who laughs at himself never runs out of things to laugh at". So my advice is to find friends with a great sense of humor who get you and can laugh with you.

Our inner circle shapes our mindsets and actions. Look for those who inspire, motivate, and uplift you. Embark on a journey of growth, contribution, and achievement together, making a difference with your life.

Go Forth

Now it's up to you...

Conclusion

There you have it. These are my ideas for nursing tips and hacks, especially for new nurses. I hope you have enjoyed reading this as much as I enjoyed writing it and that it has given you food for thought on loving your nursing profession.

By following these practices of cultivating compassion, maintaining a work-life balance, embracing continuous learning, staying positive and being resilient, fostering gratitude, finding your niche, and building friendships, new nurses can embark on a fulfilling and fun career that brings joy, satisfaction and meaningful connections with patients and colleagues alike. Getting paid for a job you love and derive meaning from and making a positive difference in people's lives is a recipe for success, happiness, and fulfillment. I wish you a career you can look back on with pride and a feeling of achievement. I wish you no regrets. Happy Nursing!

If you found this book helpful, I'd be very appreciative if you left a favorable review on Amazon.

Resources

Quoteresearch. (2014, September 2). *Choose a job you love, and you will never have to work a day in your life – quote Investigator®.* https://quoteinvestigator.com/2014/09/02/job-love/

OpenAI. (2024). *ChatGPT* (3.5) [Large language model]. https://chat.openai.com

A quote by Fred Rogers. (n.d.). https://www.goodreads.com/quotes/198594-when-i-was-a-boy-and-i-would-see-scary

AMFConsulting. (n.d.). *Have you ever heard the saying, "You are the sum of the 5 people you hang around with"?* https://www.linkedin.com/pulse/have-you-ever-heard-saying-sum-5-people-hang

A quote by Epictetus. (n.d.). https://www.goodreads.com/quotes/140577-he-who-laughs-at-himself-never-runs-out-of-things

<a href="https://www.dreamstime.com/newborn-smiling-stock-photos-image-free-5230423">5230423</a> © <a

Made in the USA
Las Vegas, NV
06 December 2024

13483338R00017